First published in Great Britain 2023 by Farshore
An imprint of HarperCollins*Publishers*
1 London Bridge Street, London SE1 9GF
www.farshore.co.uk

HarperCollins*Publishers*
Macken House, 39/40 Mayor Street Upper, Dublin 1, D01 C9W8, Ireland

Written by Laura Jackson.

ISBN 978 0 00 859113 7
Printed in Romania
001

A CIP catalogue record for this title is available from the British Library.

Parental guidance is advised for all craft and colouring activities.
Always ask an adult to help when using glue, paint and scissors. Wear protective
clothing and cover surfaces to avoid staining.

Stay safe online. Farshore is not responsible for content hosted by third parties.

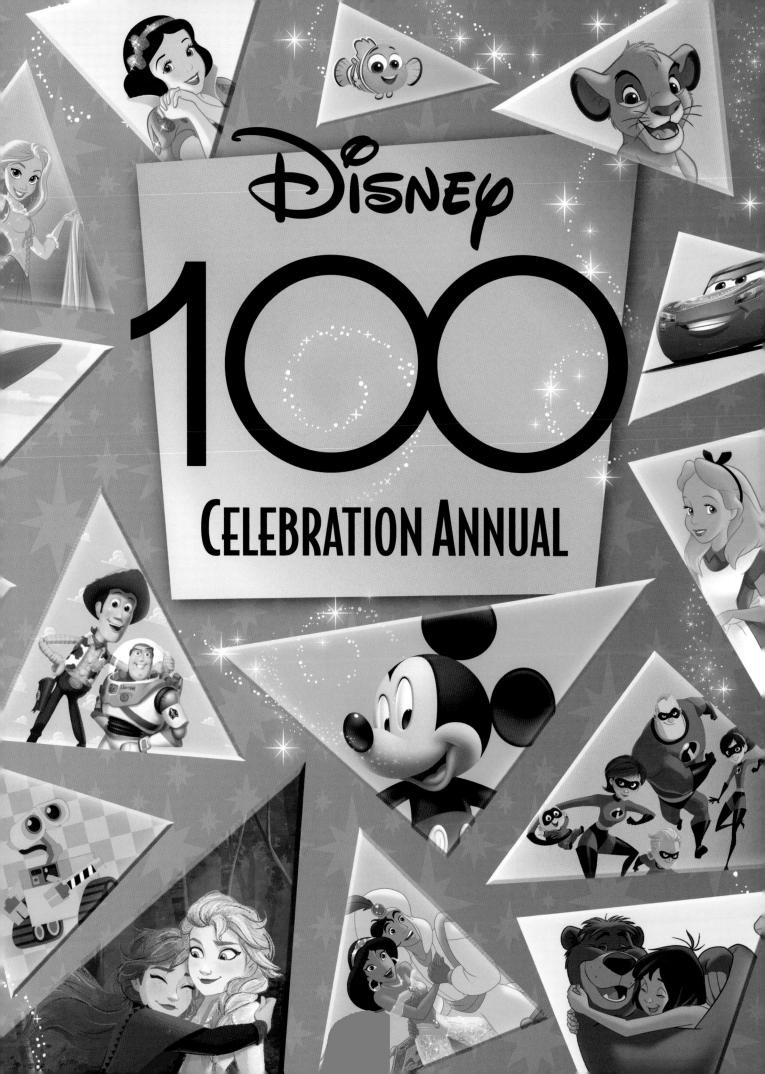

DISNEP
100
CELEBRATION ANNUAL

Contents

This Annual celebrates 100 years of much-loved Disney Characters.

Make a Wish

Look out for this star in this book. When you see one, wish upon the star.

My Favourite Disney ...

Welcome to the Disney 100 Celebration Annual!

In 2023, Disney enters its 100th year of bringing magic and joy to fans of all ages. Join the wonder with this special Annual filled with some of your favourite characters, stories, and adventures from across Disney's spectacular collection.

When you've read the classic retellings of many beloved films, completed activities and quizzes, created fantastic drawings and more, write out all your favourite things.

Favourite movie:

....

....

Favourite character:

Sophie/Harry potter

mum mrs bill

Favourite animal:

....
panda then panda
panda y ....

Favourite song:

you belong with me
stick season
billybilly rock billy
billy row taklt
easy

Favourite costume:

....
Jo gging suite Shorts
Shorts & teShirts

Favourite place:

stornaway

Draw yourself as a Disney hero or villain!

Super Soapsturl? Soccer Star

swaswa

Disney Through the Years

1923
Walt Disney and his brother Roy establish the **Disney Brothers Cartoon Studio** in Hollywood, Los Angeles.

1928
Walt Disney creates the character **Mickey Mouse**, and *Steamboat Willie* is released – the first cartoon with synchronised sound.

1937
Disney releases its first feature film, *Snow White and the Seven Dwarfs*, which became an international hit and an instant classic.

1955
Walt Disney's dream of building a theme park comes true with the opening of **Disneyland** in Anaheim, California.

1926
The company moves to Silver Lake, in Los Angeles, and changes its name to **The Walt Disney Studio.**

1950
Disney releases its first fully live-action feature, *Treasure Island.*

1964
Mary Poppins becomes Disney's most successful film up to this point and it **wins 5** Academy Awards®.

1923   1926   1928   1937   1950   1955   1964

1971

Walt Disney World in Orlando, Florida opens in honour of **Walt Disney,** who died in 1966.

1995

Toy Story is released, the first feature-length film of Pixar Animation Studios and **the first completely computer-animated feature film ever.**

1983

The **Disney Channel** begins broadcasting.

2013

Frozen becomes a worldwide hit, and **wins 2** Academy Awards®.

1987

The first *Disney Store* opened at Glendale Galleria in California.

2019

Disney+ launches, Disney's first **streaming platform.**

1992

Disneyland Paris opens.

2023

Disney celebrates it's **100th Anniversary.**

| 1971 | 1983 | 1987 | 1992 | 1995 | 2013 | 2019 | 2023 |

Party Problem

Mickey and Minnie are ready to celebrate, but they've lost Pluto. Help them through the maze to find their missing dog and get them to the party on time! Pick up Donald and Daisy on the way.

START →

FINISH

Answers on page 116.

Mickey's Wordsearch

Find the names of Mickey and his friends in the grid.
Look up, down, forwards and backwards.

X	P	A	E	L	D	R	Z	E	Q
M	E	W	X	W	O	T	T	R	U
I	Y	L	M	I	N	N	I	E	F
C	K	S	O	G	A	X	C	I	J
K	U	P	Z	R	L	W	T	U	H
E	M	L	N	U	D	A	I	S	Y
Y	E	U	B	H	S	S	Q	Y	E
T	O	T	U	M	G	A	W	D	I
Y	F	O	O	G	Z	T	L	E	A
E	W	H	Q	Z	X	A	Y	J	E

MICKEY   GOOFY

MINNIE   DONALD

PLUTO   DAISY

Answers on page 116.

Super Sizes

The jungle is filled with creatures big and small!

1. Circle the **biggest**.

2. Circle the **smallest**.

3. Number these characters up from **biggest** to **smallest**.

4. Number these characters up from **smallest** to **biggest**.

Answers on page 116.

Animal Alphabet

Fill in the missing letters of these Jungle Book animals.

snake

monkey

panther

bear

elephant

Answers on page 116.

Follow Your Heart

Aladdin loves going on adventures with Jasmine. Which path will take him to her?

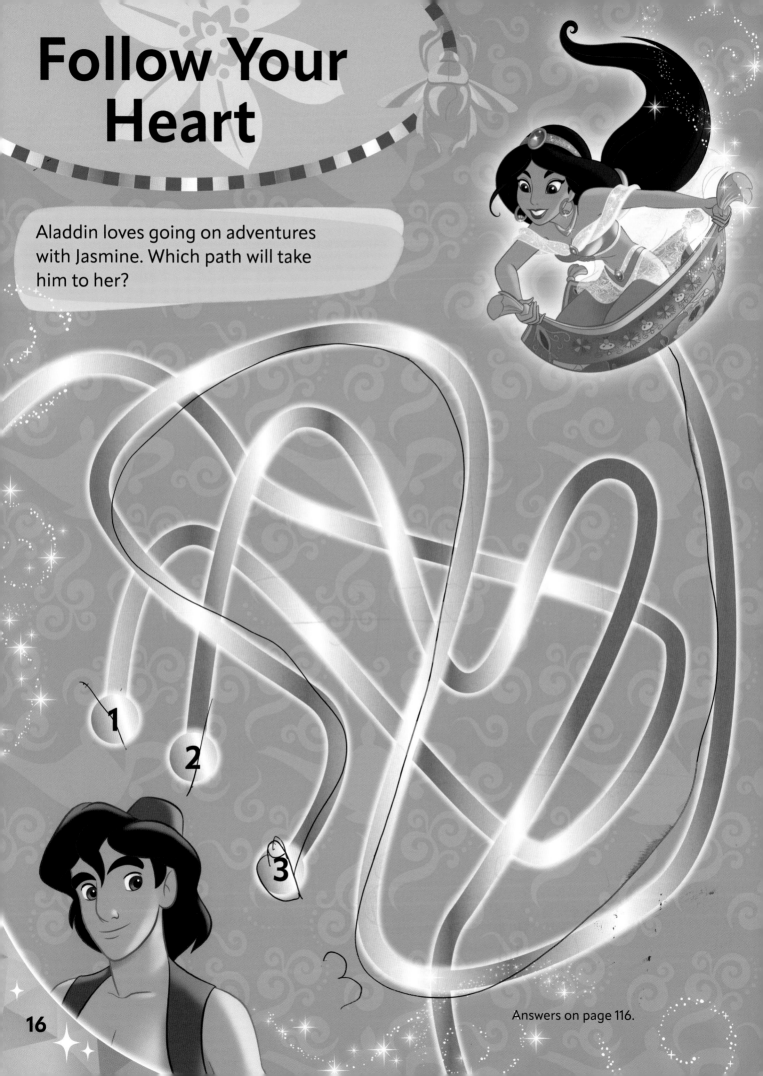

1

2

3

Answers on page 116.

Magic Count

Count the lamps in the market. The Genie's magic lamp is also hiding. Circle it when you see it!

I count ｜0 lamps, including the Genie's lamp!

Answers on page 116.

Down the Rabbit Hole

Help Alice find her way through the twisty-turny rabbit hole to catch up with the White Rabbit. Stay away from the Queen of Hearts!

START

FINISH

Answers on page 116.

Tricky Stripes

Alice needs help but the Cheshire Cat is fooling around! Join the dots and colour him in to make him complete.

Don't forget to add his stripes!

Puppy Pairs

Perdita and Pongo are trying to round up their noisy pups before they scamper away. Match the puppies into pairs. Shout out 'Woof, woof!' each time you find a pair.

1

2

3

4

5

6

7

8

9

a

e

b

c

f

h

d

g

i

Answers on page 116.

101 Dalmatians

Listen to the story about the spotty pups.
When you see a picture, join in and say the word.

Cruella De Vil   puppies

spotty   Perdita   Pongo

 was a mean person. One day, she ordered two

men to steal fifteen Dalmatian . She wanted to use

their fur to make expensive coats!

The pups' parents and looked everywhere

for the , but they just couldn't find them. Word

spread across London from dog to dog, and soon

everyone was looking for the missing .

With a lot of help, and finally found the

 hidden in a big, old house belonging to .

But imagine their surprise, when they found not just

their own , but another 84 !

 and quietly guided all 101 away from

the house, but and the mean men were hot on their tails. How would and get all those   to safety?

They hid under bridges, down frozen rivers and even inside a barn, but and the men were still chasing them. When it seemed like there was no escape, the came up a plan.

While and her men weren't looking, all the rolled in black soot, completely covering up their coats. Now they were in disguise.

Sure enough, didn't recognise the little black dogs racing past. The had escaped. They were safe, at last.

Now  and had to come up with a new plan – how to look after 101  .

Woof! Woof!

Starry Shadows

The friends are going for a starry sky-high adventure in Never Land. Draw lines to match the friends to their silhouettes. Watch out for Captain Hook hiding in the shadows too!

Answers on page 116.

Tinker Bell Trails

Captain Hook is on the attack. Help Tinker Bell find an escape route by using a pencil to carefully follow the trail to Peter. If you crash into the sides, Hook might see you and you will have to start again!

Pinocchio Patterns

Come and meet Pinocchio and his friends. Can you work out what is missing in each pattern row?

1

   **?**

2

    **?**

3

   **?**

Answers on page 116.

Puzzle Pals

Pinocchio has fun wherever he goes.
Can you find the close-ups in the big picture?

Answers on page 116.

Beautiful Butterfly

All the butterflies love playing with Bambi. Can you finish the other half of this fluttery butterfly?

Then add some bright colours to your butterfly.

The Way Back Home

Bambi fell asleep and now he's lost in the forest. Guide him safely back to his mum following Bambi's friends in this order:

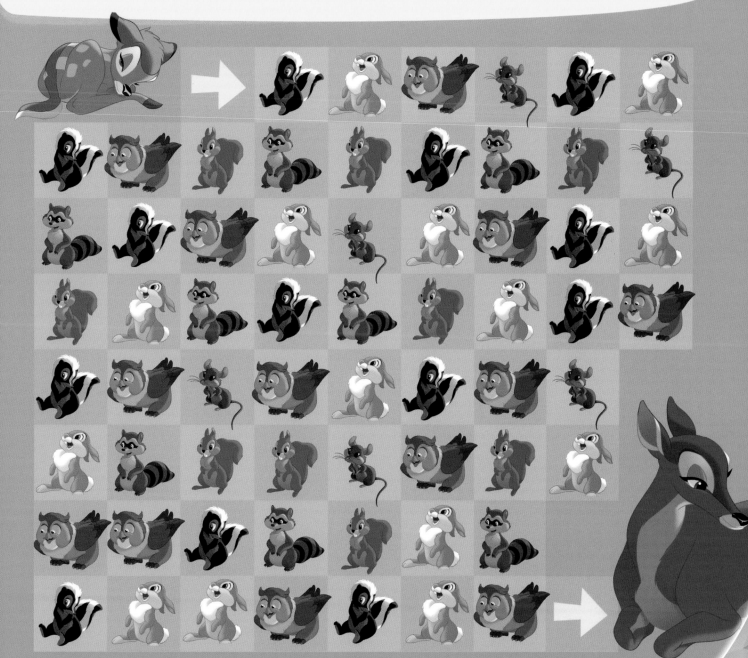

Answers on page 116.

The Lion King

As the sun rose over the African
Pride Lands, a new baby lion was born.
King Mufasa and Queen Sarabi were
ready to show their baby to the world.
Every animal had come to celebrate
baby Simba, who would one day
be their king.

There was just one animal who
had not come to honour the birth.
Scar, Mufasa's brother, was jealous
of Simba and stayed away.

30

Time passed happily, and Simba grew into a curious cub.

"One day, the sun will set on my time here," said Mufasa, "and will rise with you as the new king."

Simba gazed over at the dark lands in the distance. "But you must never go there," Mufasa warned his son.

Meanwhile, Scar was growing more and more jealous of Simba, and he hatched a plan.

"Only the bravest lions go there," Scar purred, pointing towards the shadowy place.

He knew Simba wanted to be brave, just like his dad.

The next day, the little cub bounced off to find his best friend, Nala. Simba persuaded her to explore the dark place with him.

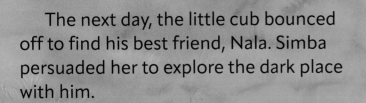

When they arrived, it was eerie and quiet but Simba and Nala were not alone. Three hyenas sprang out, ready to attack.

Mufasa suddenly thundered towards them and slammed the hyenas into the ground.

In all the chaos, nobody noticed Scar in the shadows. He was already forming a new plan. A plan from which neither Simba nor Mufasa could escape alive.

The very next day, Scar set to work. He lured Simba to a deep gorge and let a herd of wildebeest stampede at him.

Little Simba clung onto a branch, until mighty Mufasa roared to the rescue once again.

Simba was safe, but Mufasa was not. A wildebeest crashed into him, and Mufasa slid off the cliff.

"Brother – help me!" Mufasa called up to Scar.

"Long live the king," Scar sneered, as he let Mufasa fall to his death.

Simba cried and cried for his beloved father.

"If it weren't for you, he would still be alive," said Scar. "Run away, Simba, and never return!"

Confused and heartbroken, Simba fled.

Scar took Mufasa's place as king, and a new cruel rule took over the Pride Lands. Hyenas prowled, plants and trees died, and nobody had enough food.

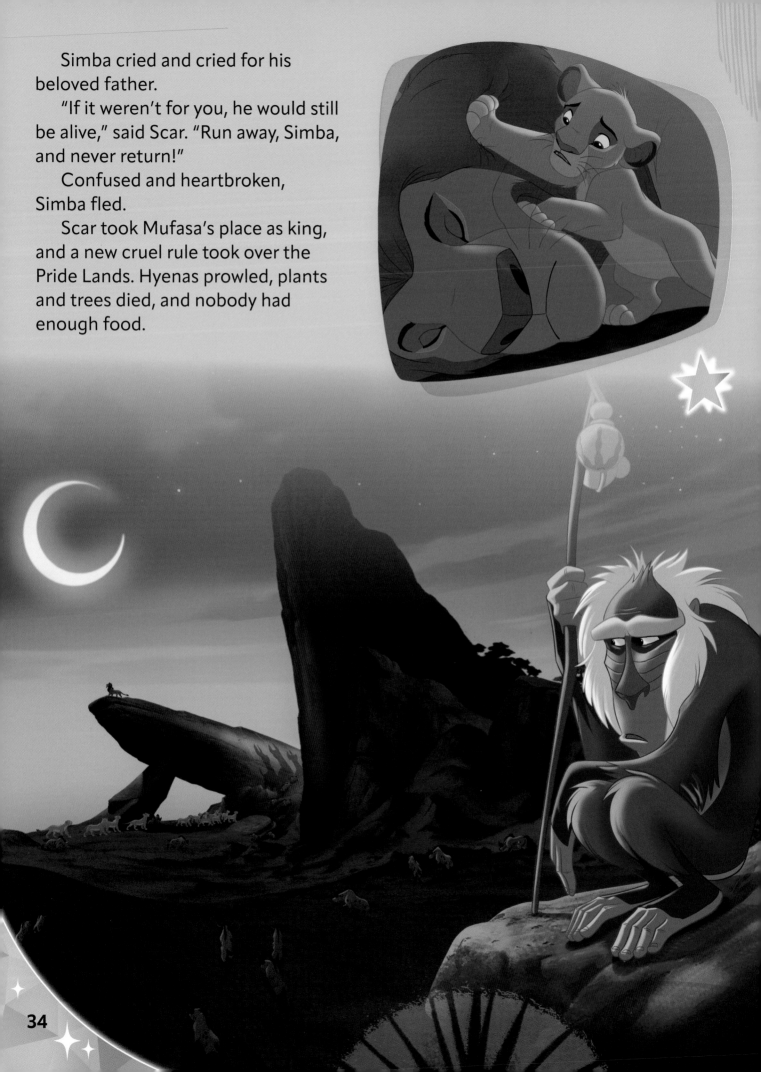

Years passed and Simba grew into a strong lion. He lived far away, with Timon, a cheeky meerkat and Pumbaa, a kind warthog.

They taught Simba to live with no rules, no responsibilities and no worries!

"Hakuna Matata!" they would sing.

Simba seemed happy, but he had a deep sadness inside.

One afternoon, a lioness prowled into Simba's home. It was Nala!

"Everyone thought you were dead!" Nala gasped. "But as you're alive, YOU should be king, not Scar!"

Simba was afraid to go back to the Pride Lands, but he knew that his father would want him to be brave.

When he finally reached the Pride Lands, Simba was horrified. The land was bare and dry.

"Step down, Scar," Simba roared angrily into the night.

Scar was shocked that Simba was alive, but he was not going to give up without a fight.

"It's your fault Mufasa is dead," spat Scar.

Hyenas circled, and pushed Simba to the edge of the cliff. Then Scar whispered and smiled, "I killed Mufasa."

Finding a strength deep inside, Simba lunged at Scar. This time, Scar plunged backwards.

"Run away and never return!" roared Simba.

Rain began to fall and thunder rolled. Simba looked to the sky and remembered everything his father had taught him.

The king had returned.

Under Simba's rule, the Pride Lands flourished.

And one morning, as the sun rose in the sky, Nala and Simba's baby cub was born.

The circle of life was complete.

Story Quiz

How much can you remember about The Lion King story? Take the quiz to find out.

1 Who wouldn't celebrate the birth of Simba?

a Mufasa

b Nala

c Scar

2 What animals tried to attack Simba and Nala?

a hyenas

b zebras

c warthogs

3 Who killed Mufasa?

a Simba

b Scar

c hyenas

4 What animal did Simba live with when he ran away?

a a meerkat

b a giraffe

a a bird

5 Who is Scar?

a Mufasa's brother

b Simba's dad

c Nala's brother

Answers on page 116.

Count Along

Simba and his friends are ready to play but the hyenas are on the prowl. Count up each animal type to keep them safe.

Write how many animals you can count below.

3

5

2

6

7

4

9

Answers on page 116.

Jigsaw Jumble

Lady's family photograph is in a big jumble. Draw lines to show where each piece belongs in the puzzle.

Answers on page 116.

Paper Chains

Make these paper chains with an adult and decorate your room!

 Cut out the paper strips – make some more with your own paper and pens.

 Take one strip and curl it around in a circle and glue the two ends together.

 Feed your next strip through the middle of the first, curl round and glue the two ends together.

 Repeat until you have linked all the strips and hang your finished festive paper chain.

© Disney

© Disney

Pet Puzzle

Picture key:

Draw lines from each picture in the key to show where it belongs on the grid. Each picture should appear only once in every column, row and square of four.

Answers on page 116.

Dumbo Design

Can you draw little Dumbo into the second grid?
Copy the picture, square by square.

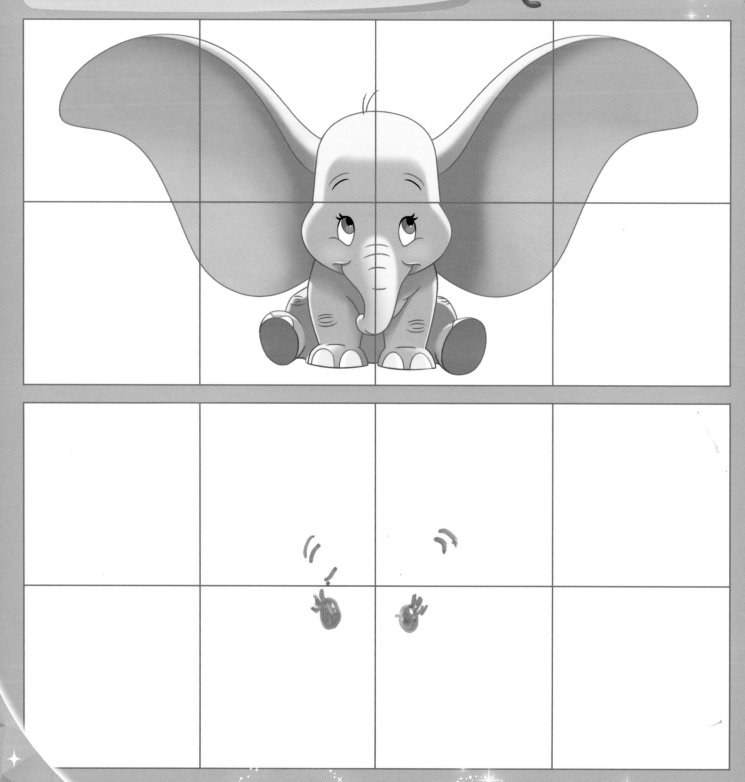

Believe in Yourself!

The Circle of Life

Wish Upon a Star

Trace around the big wishing star. Use the design ideas to fill your star with fun patterns and colours.

Starry design ideas:

Go dotty

Go stripy

Go zigzag

Go swirly

Now make a wish upon your star!

47

Meet the Madrigals

Mirabel
Growing up in a family of heroes can be hard, but Mirabel does everything she can to make her family proud.

The Madrigals are one big, noisy, extraordinary family. Let's learn all about them and their special powers.

Abuela Alma
Abuela brought magic to the family many years ago. She leads her family through good times and bad.

Julieta
Mother to Mirabel, Luisa and Isabela, Julieta loves to care for her family with delicious food.

Agustín
Mirabel's father always tries to make his family happy. He spreads fun and kindness wherever he goes.

Bruno
The Madrigals don't talk about Bruno. He ran away from his family many years ago.

Magic Gift
I see into the future.

Magic Gift
I make food to heal people.

Pepa

Wild and wonderful Pepa has big emotions. She is a whirl of energy and her family love her sunny and stormy ways.

Félix

Félix puts the fun into every party he goes to. Everybody wants to be around funny Félix!

Isabela

Beautiful Isabela is the golden child, but she secretly finds it hard to be perfect all the time.

Magic Gift
I make flowers bloom.

Magic Gift
I can control the weather.

Dolores

Ssshhh … If there is a secret in the Encanto, Dolores will be the first to find out and the first to pass the secret on!

Antonio

Mirabel's little cousin is sweet and gentle. He has a special connection with animals big and small.

Magic Gift
I have superhuman hearing.

Luisa

Luisa can lift two donkeys! She likes to help everyone – no job is too big for mighty Luisa.

Magic Gift
I have super strength.

Magic Gift
I can communicate with animals.

Camilo

Camilo is a master of trickery and storytelling who is not afraid to speak the truth.

Magic Gift
I can shapeshift.

49

Stronger Together

Mirabel loves living in Casita with her sisters. They might have their differences but together they can do anything. Can you spot 5 differences in picture 2?

Answers on page 117.

Magical Madrigal Memory

There is fun, secrets and magic everywhere in the Encanto! Look carefully at this picture. Now cover it up with some paper and see how much you can remember.

Circle the right answer to each question.

1	Antonio is riding a jaguar.	True	False
2	Isabella's dress is yellow.	True	False
3	There is a waterfall in the picture.	True	False
4	Mirabel isn't in the picture.	True	False
5	Three capybaras are sat on the hill.	True	False

Answers on page 117.

Which Friend Are You?

Have you ever wondered which Disney character you are most like?
Take the quiz to find out!

1 Where would you love to live?

a anywhere as long as you're with your family
b in a big, beautiful city
c by the ocean
d in a snowy land
e on an island

2 What word most describes you?

a fearless
b cheeky
c determined
d funny
e loud

3 When I am in danger, I:

a face it, head on
b hide in the shadows
c ask for help
d ruuuuunnnn!
e fight back

4 What would your sidekick be?

a all my family!
b a mischievous monkey
c a friendly fish
d a strong reindeer
e I am just fine on my own!

5 What is the best motto for you?

a protect those you love
b think quick, stay smart
c never stop exploring
d stay happy!
e be the best

6 What is your favourite activity?

a sky diving
b hunting for old treasure
c discovering new things
d snowball fighting
e surfing

Mostly **a**s
You are Elastigirl
You are smart, strong and super to your friends and family! Always giving little fist bumps of support to everyone around you, you are the ultimate protector.

7 **What do you like to do with your friends?**

a have a running race
b play hide-and-seek
c sing
d give big hugs
e play funny tricks

Mostly **b**s
You are Aladdin
As a cheeky adventurer always on the lookout for mischief, you are a whirlwind of fun and chaos.

Mostly **C**s
You are Ariel
You love singing, exploring and meeting new friends. Even when things don't always go to plan, you never, ever give up.

8 **What would be your biggest wish?**

a to fight crime and bring peace everywhere
b to fly
c to live in the ocean and on the land
d to control weather
e to shapeshift

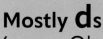

Mostly **d**s
You are Olaf
You are a lovable friend, and everyone loves hanging out with you. Always up for fun and silliness, you make the world a brighter place.

9 **What is your favourite type of movie?**

a action
b adventure
c musical
d comedy
e hero

Mostly **e**s
You are Maui
You are a super-strong trickster and a hurricane of energy. You can sometimes lose your temper if things go wrong, but underneath it all you are a softie!

53

Tell the Time

Tiana is having a busy evening meeting up with her friends. Draw the hands on the clock faces to show when she meets each friend.

At **6 o'clock** Tiana and Lottie try on their festival outfits.

At **7 o'clock** Tiana helps Louis practise his horn.

At **8 o'clock** Naveen and Tiana meet up for their favourite dance.

Answers on page 117.

Party Prep

Tiana is hosting a party and there is so much to do. Can you help her think up some party food and draw it on the plate?

A Christmas Wish

Snow White and the friends are decorating the tree and making Christmas wishes. Put the pictures in the correct order by writing the numbers in the boxes below.

Answers on page 117.

Who's Who?

Draw a line to match Snow White's friends to the correct close-up pictures below.

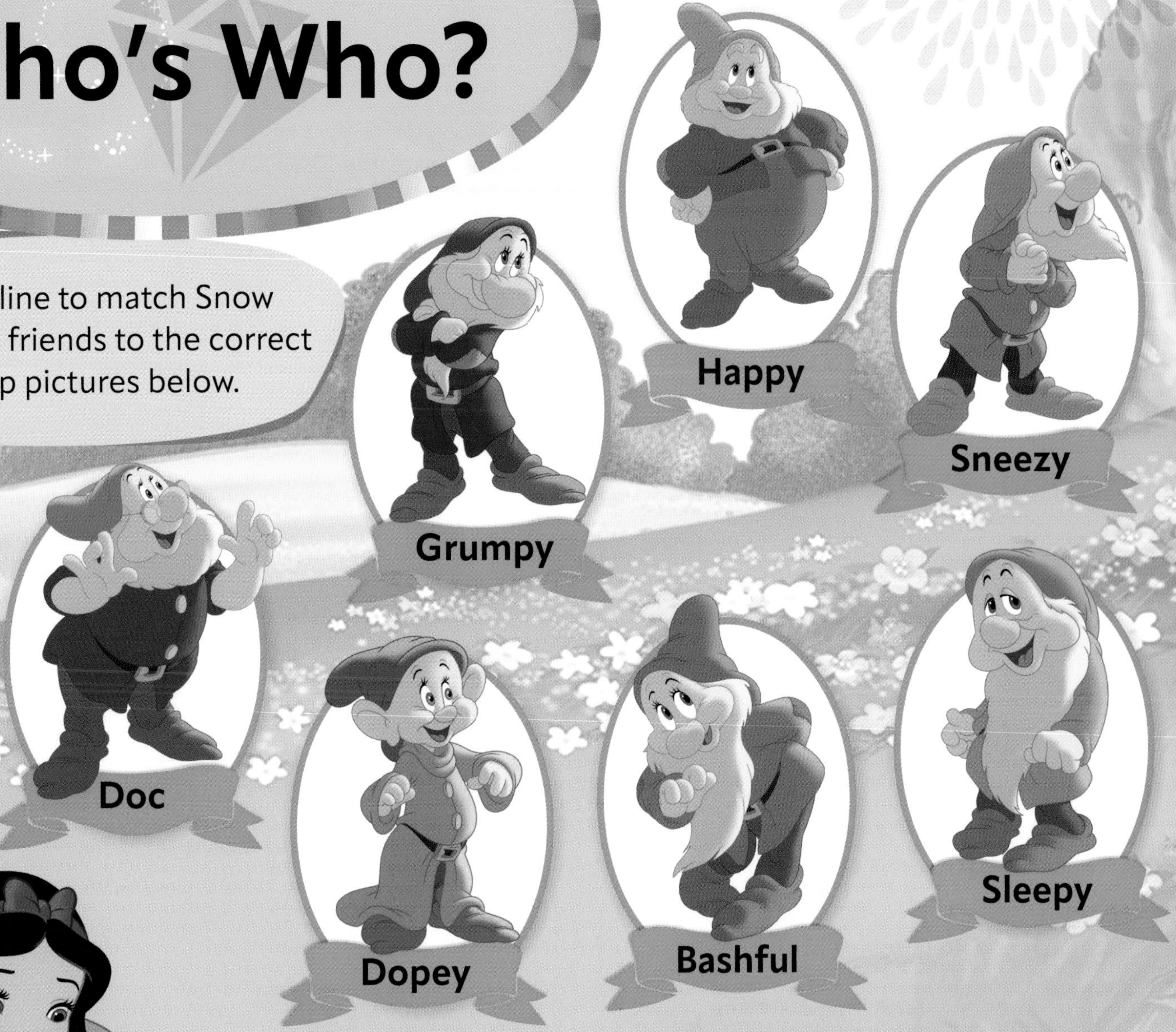
Happy
Grumpy
Sneezy
Doc
Dopey
Bashful
Sleepy

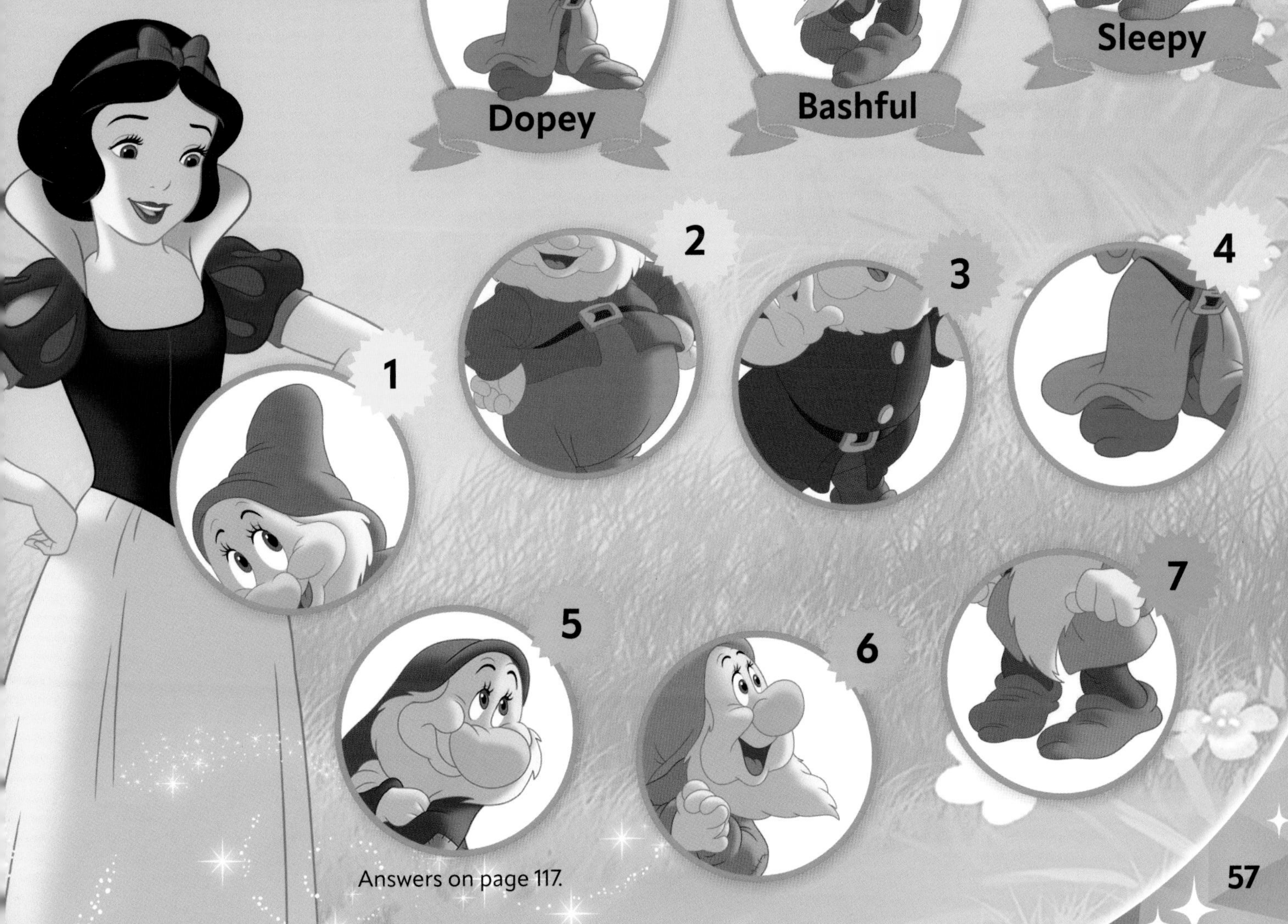
1
2
3
4
5
6
7

Answers on page 117.

Cinderella

Once upon a time, there lived a kind girl called Cinderella. Poor Cinderella had a hard life.

She lived with her cruel stepmother and stepsisters. They made Cinderella cook, clean, scrub and sweep for every hour of every day.

No matter how hard things got, Cinderella would always find happiness with her animal friends.

She just knew in her heart that the world was still a good place.

One day, a letter arrived. It was an invitation to the Royal Ball.
The stepsisters squealed with excitement. They were sure the handsome Prince would fall in love with one of them!

The sisters did not want Cinderella to go to the ball. They gave her so much work to do, Cinderella didn't have any time to get her dress ready.

While Cinderella cleaned and cooked all day for the mean sisters, her loyal animal friends set to work themselves. They sewed and stitched and styled until Cinderella had a new ballgown that was truly wonderful!

When the stepsisters saw Cinderella in her new dress, they flew into a jealous rage. Cinderella simply looked too pretty, too perfect. They ripped the dress to shreds.

Cinderella's dream of going to the ball was over. She fled into the garden and cried. "There is nothing left to believe in," she said. "Nothing!"

But there was something magical brewing in the air. A swirl of sparkles twirled through the mist ...

Cinderella's Fairy Godmother appeared! She waved her wand and told Cinderella she would go to the ball.

"Bibbidi-bobbidi-boo!" sang the Fairy Godmother.

Lots of things happened all at once. A pumpkin turned into a carriage, the mice turned into horses and then the best thing of all ...

Cinderella's dress transformed into a beautiful blue gown with a pair of sparkling glass slippers.

"It's like a dream," gasped Cinderella.

"Like all dreams, this can't last forever," warned Fairy Godmother.

Cinderella had to be home by midnight, when the magic would disappear.

As Cinderella arrived at the palace, the ballroom was awash with swirling dresses, soft music and twinkling candles.

Cinderella's stepsisters were busy trying to make the Prince notice them, but he had eyes for only one person ... Cinderella.

Cinderella and the Prince danced around the ballroom for hours and walked together under the moonlight. They were quickly falling in love. Soon, it was nearly midnight. The magic was about to end.

"Goodbye!" Cinderella called out to the Prince, and quickly hurried away. The Prince ran after her but she was gone, leaving one glass slipper behind.

The next day, word had spread that the Prince wanted to meet the mysterious girl from the ball. The Grand Duke went from door to door to find the owner of the glass slipper.

Cinderella's stepmother was cunning. She quickly realised Cinderella was the secret girl at the ball and so she locked her away. Now the Prince could never find his true love!

"Let me out!" cried Cinderella.

When the Grand Duke arrived at the door, the stepmother was hoping one of her daughters' feet would fit into Cinderella's glass slipper.

Squeeze! Squish! Squash! It was no use. The daughters' feet would not fit into Cinderella's glass slipper.

As the Duke turned to leave, he heard a small voice behind him.

"May I try it on?" It was Cinderella! Her loyal animal friends had helped her to escape.

The slipper was a perfect fit. Cinderella was free!

Cinderella and the Prince were a perfect match and they soon got married, much to the delight of Cinderella's animal friends.

Never again did Cinderella have to clean or cook for her stepmother or stepsisters. All her wishes had come true, and she lived happily and freely for ever more.

Helpful Friends

Cinderella has many animal friends, and they all want to help her out.

1 Find the five pairs of matching birds.

2 One of the birds has an invitation for the ball. Can you find it?

3 Can you spot the bird carrying a beautiful ring for Cinderella?

Answers on page 117.

Swirl and Twirl

Cinderella has been invited to a winter party. Colour and decorate her outfit with icy blue, purple and silver crayons.

Trace over the snowflakes to make it snow!

Belle's World

Follow the trail and meet Belle and all her friends.

Phillippe

Belle's loyal horse is one of the family, but if wolves are on the prowl Phillippe has been known to run far, far away!

Belle

Belle is forever reading books and dreaming of adventures. She finds the good in everyone, even the grumpy Beast!

Maurice

Belle's father has some funny ways, and not everyone understands him. But Maurice doesn't care! He is way too busy inventing the next big thing.

The Beast

Living alone in his castle, the Beast can seem angry and rude to the townspeople. But Belle unlocks a kindness hidden inside him.

Mrs Potts

Mrs Potts is the castle's housekeeper and she makes sure everything is in order. She is never afraid to speak her mind, even to the Beast.

Chip

This little teacup loves to explore with Belle. He might be small, but Chip is one of Belle's bravest friends.

Wardrobe

Big on fashion, the Wardrobe has an outfit for every occasion. Her doors are always open and ready to help her friends in the castle.

Lumière

Bright and happy Lumière lights his own path and follows his own rules. He is in love with the idea of love, even if he doesn't always understand it.

Cogsworth

Cogsworth runs the castle with Mrs Potts. He can be bossy, but only because he is scared the Beast might shout if things go wrong!

Belle's Rose

There are many different flowers, but the rose is Belle's favourite!

1 ADD up these flower sums.

a  =

b =

c =

2 FINISH the colour sequence below.

3 COLOUR Lumière and TRACE his flames.

Answers on page 117.

A Snowy Mission

Belle needs to find the Beast but there is a swirling snowstorm. Which trail will lead Belle to the Beast? Stay away from Gaston and Le Fou!

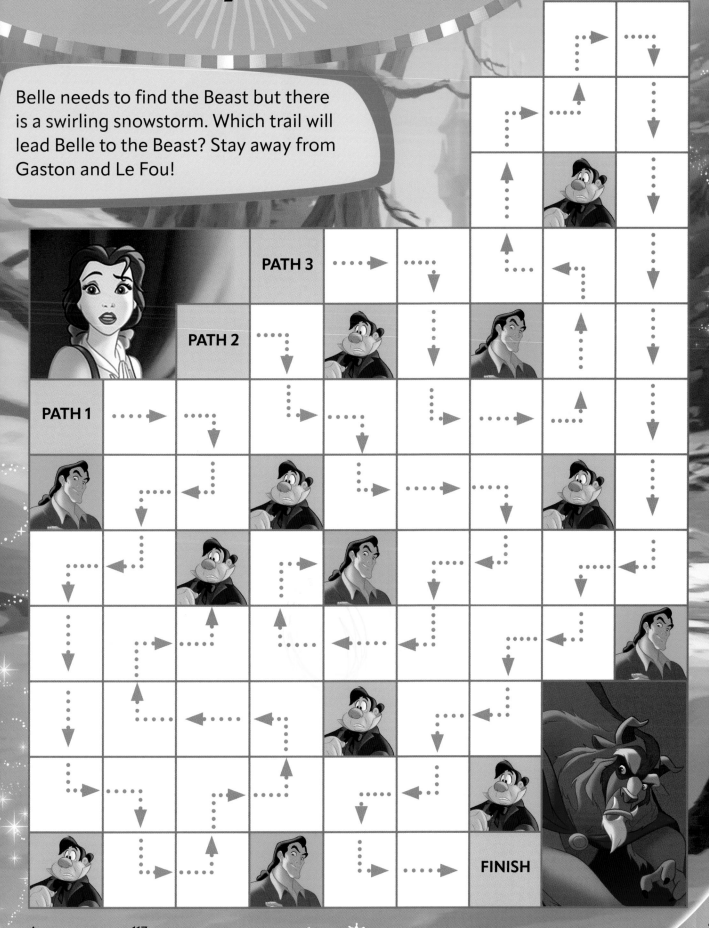

FINISH

Odd One Out

Moana loves living on the island of Motunui with her family, friends and pets. Can you spot the odd one out in each group?

Answers on page 117.

Make a Splash

Moana wishes she could adventure far into the ocean. Use the small picture to help you colour the big picture and make her wishes come true!

Trace the lines to make more splashes.

73

The Little Mermaid

Find out all about Ariel's wishes and dreams. When you see a picture join in and say the word!

Ariel   Flounder

King Triton   Prince Eric   waves   ship   treasure

Deep under the , lived an adventurous mermaid

called . She loved life with her family, but she

wished she could be part of the human world too.

 and her best friend  would spend hours

searching for human . "Have you ever seen

anything so wonderful?" said , as she showed

him all the  she had found.

Her father, , did not share 's curiosity.

He thought humans were dangerous, and he would

not let  go above the .

 couldn't help herself. One day, she swam

to the surface again and saw a sailing past.

On board the was .

"Isn't he handsome?" giggled .

Suddenly, thunder roared in the sky. Giant

battered against the and fell into the sea!

Beneath the , swam with all her might

and pulled to shore. sang softly to

 about wanting to be part of the human world.

When she heard humans in the distance,

quickly hid under the  once more.

 was furious when he found out what had

done. "Contact with the human world is forbidden!"

he shouted.

 loved , and she just knew she couldn't

ignore her dreams and wishes any longer. had

to follow her heart. This was just the beginning …

Finding Friends

Can you help Ariel work out which line she should follow to find her friends?

a

b

c

Answers on page 117.

Count with Ariel

Ariel treasures every single human thing she finds in the sea.
Trace the missing numbers to help Ariel along the path to the pretty necklace.

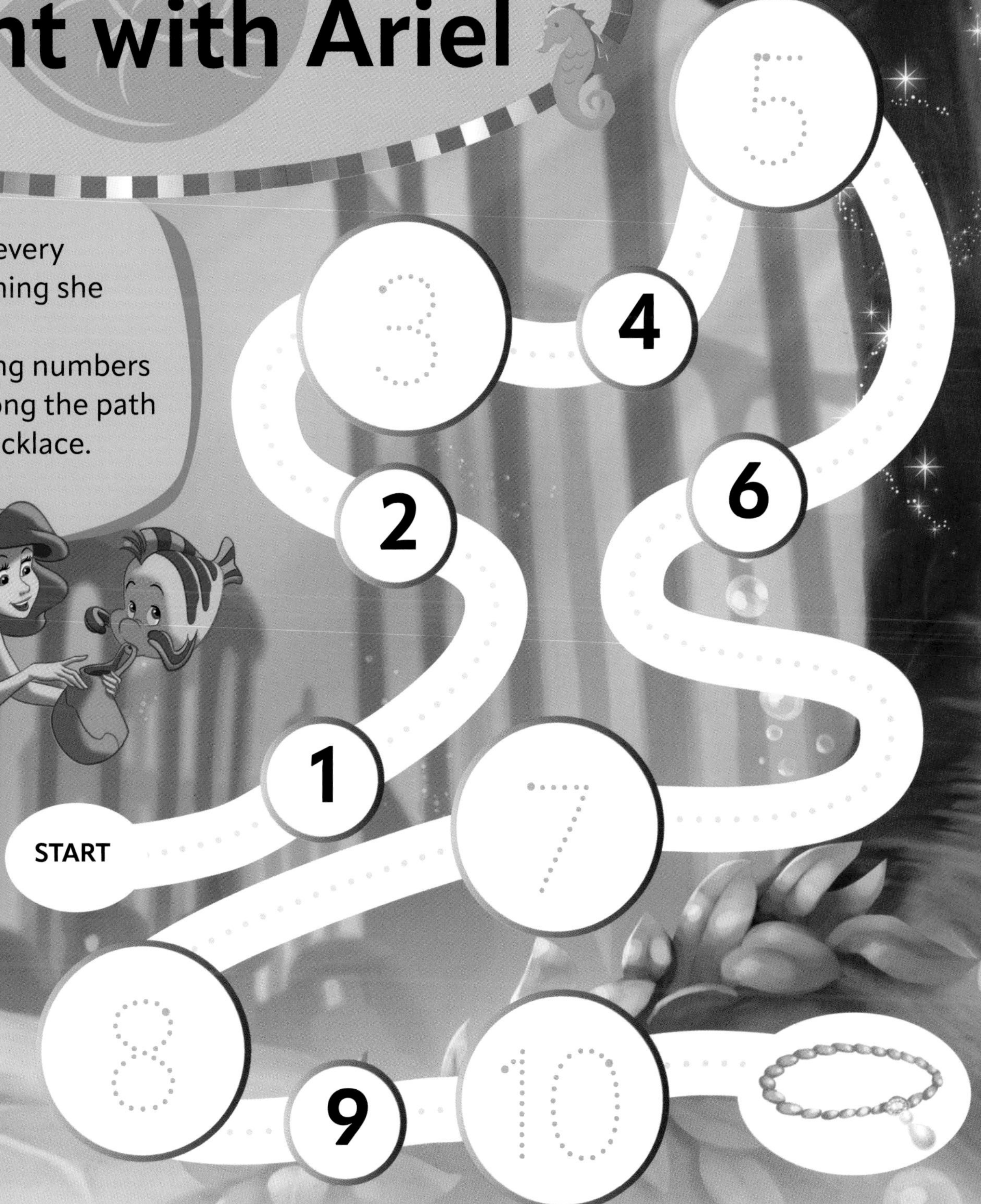

5

3

4

2

6

1

START

7

8

9

10

Count Ariel's treasures in the two boxes.
Tick ✔ the box that has the most things, a or b.

a

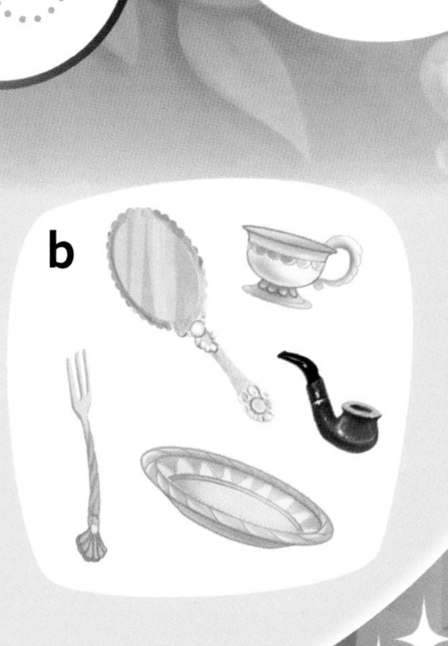

b

a

b

Answers on page 117.

Rapunzel's Round-up

Rapunzel's wish has come true. She is finally free from the tower! Round up the guests to celebrate. Can you find three-in-a-row of each friend?

Point to the friend that appears most in the grid.

Answers on page 117.

Chameleon Colours

Rapunzel and Pascal have some fun colour puzzles for you to solve.

1 CIRCLE the GREEN Pascal.

a  b c  d

2 TICK the PURPLE dress.

a  b  c  d

3 Which colour comes next in each sequence? COLOUR your answer.

a

b

c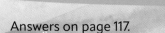

Answers on page 117.

79

Fairy Fun

Can you help Aurora solve these fun puzzles?

1 WHICH fairy comes next in this sequence?

?

2 CIRCLE the odd fairy out?

a   b   c   d

3 FIND Merryweather's shadow.

  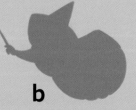 

a   b   c

Answers on page 117.

Be Your Own Hero!

Better Together!

Poster Power

Grab your crayons and colour your own power poster.

Make
Your Wishes
Come
True!

83

Toy Story

Andy was a little boy with a big imagination. He loved playing with all his toys, but his favourite toy in the world was Woody the cowboy. Andy took Woody everywhere.

One morning, when Andy was downstairs, Woody sat upright. "Ok, everyone, the coast is clear!" he said.

One by one, Andy's toys peeked out of the closet, just as they did every time there were no humans around.

Woody reminded the toys that Andy's family were moving house that week, and that Andy's birthday party was today.

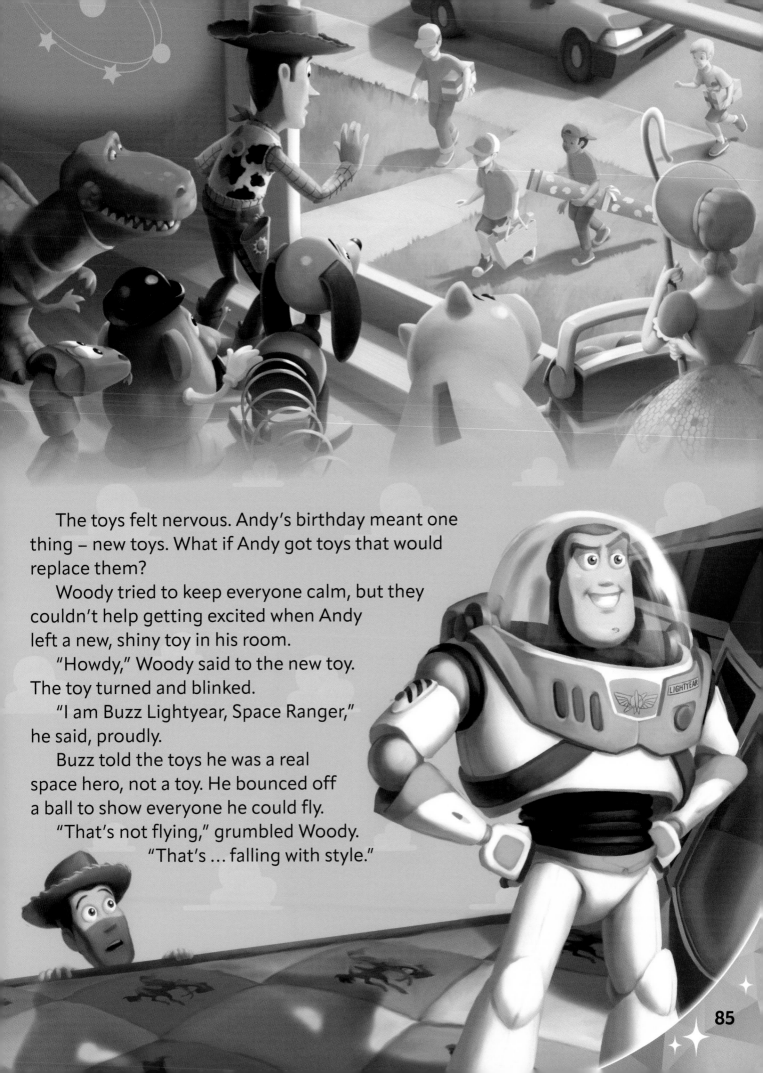

The toys felt nervous. Andy's birthday meant one thing – new toys. What if Andy got toys that would replace them?

Woody tried to keep everyone calm, but they couldn't help getting excited when Andy left a new, shiny toy in his room.

"Howdy," Woody said to the new toy. The toy turned and blinked.

"I am Buzz Lightyear, Space Ranger," he said, proudly.

Buzz told the toys he was a real space hero, not a toy. He bounced off a ball to show everyone he could fly.

"That's not flying," grumbled Woody. "That's ... falling with style."

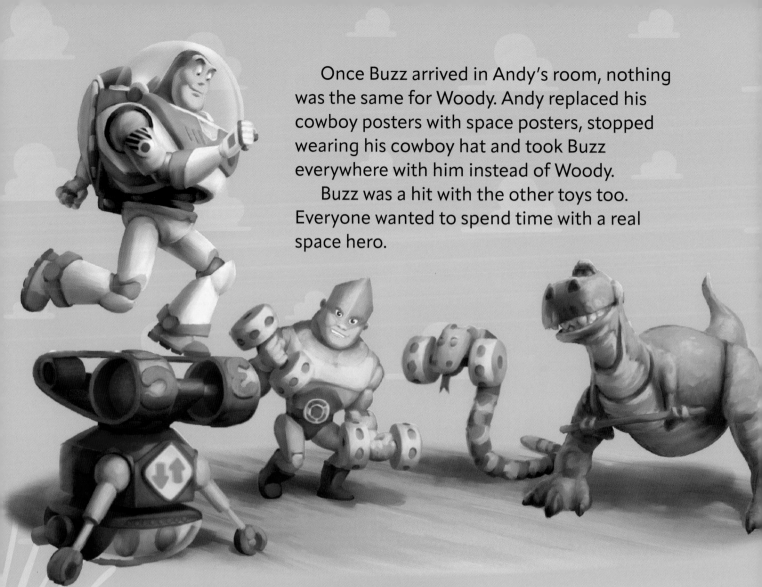

Once Buzz arrived in Andy's room, nothing was the same for Woody. Andy replaced his cowboy posters with space posters, stopped wearing his cowboy hat and took Buzz everywhere with him instead of Woody.

Buzz was a hit with the other toys too. Everyone wanted to spend time with a real space hero.

That evening, Andy was getting ready to go to Planet Pizza and he was allowed to take one toy. Woody meant to push Buzz behind the desk so Andy couldn't find him. But instead, Buzz toppled out of the window!

Before the toys could help, Andy came in and, unable to find Buzz, grabbed Woody. As the car revved up outside, a small figure rolled out of the bushes and grabbed onto the bumper. It was Buzz!

When Woody arrived at Pizza Planet, everything started to go wrong. Buzz got mad at Woody, Woody lost sight of Andy and worst of all, Andy's neighbour Sid had spied the toys.

Sid was the cruellest boy on the block. He tortured toys just for fun, and now he was taking Buzz and Woody home with him!

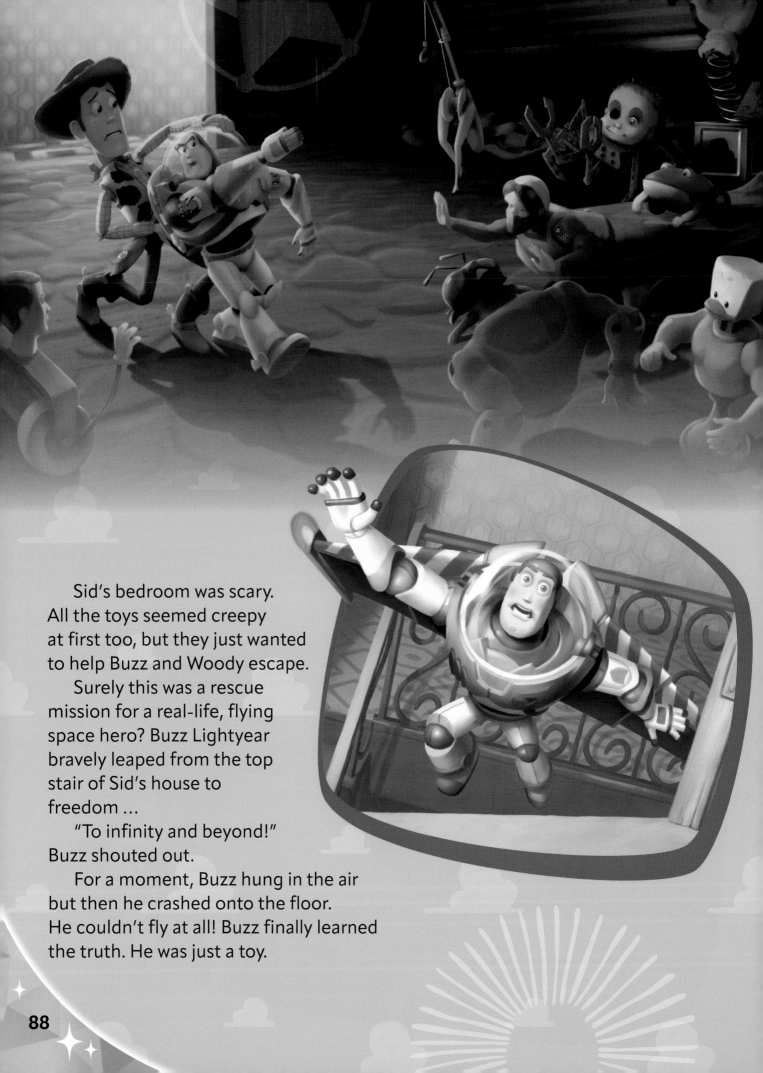

Sid's bedroom was scary.
All the toys seemed creepy
at first too, but they just wanted
to help Buzz and Woody escape.
Surely this was a rescue
mission for a real-life, flying
space hero? Buzz Lightyear
bravely leaped from the top
stair of Sid's house to
freedom …

"To infinity and beyond!"
Buzz shouted out.

For a moment, Buzz hung in the air
but then he crashed onto the floor.
He couldn't fly at all! Buzz finally learned
the truth. He was just a toy.

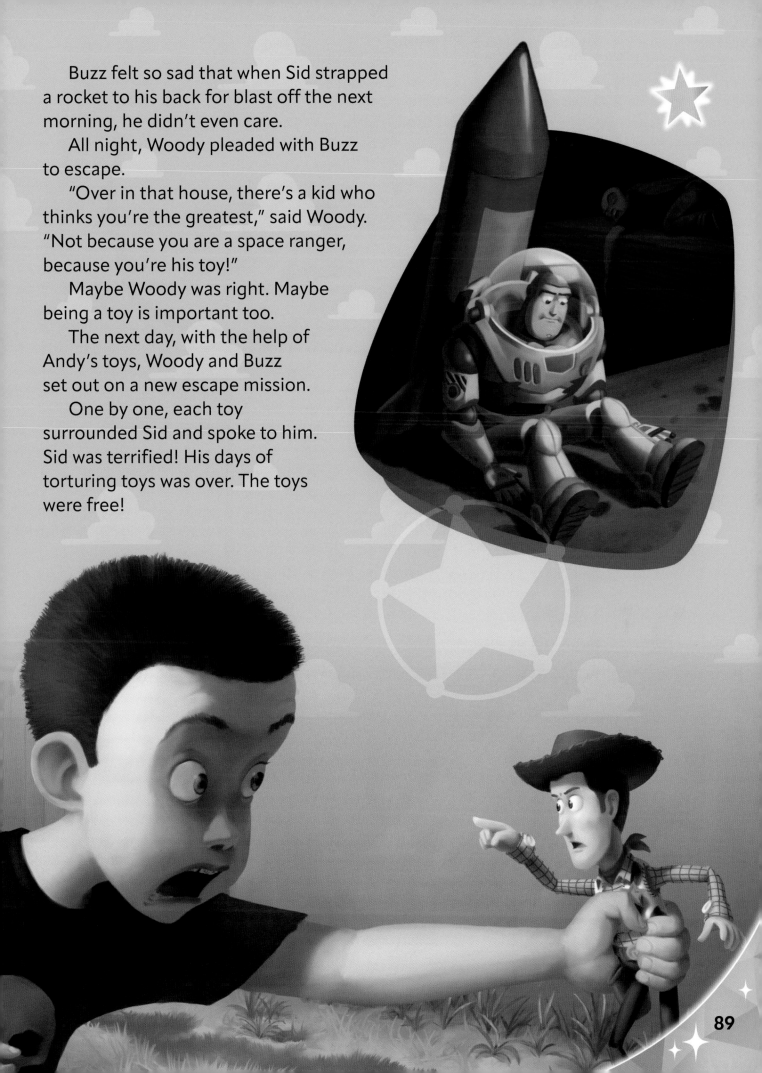

Buzz felt so sad that when Sid strapped a rocket to his back for blast off the next morning, he didn't even care.

All night, Woody pleaded with Buzz to escape.

"Over in that house, there's a kid who thinks you're the greatest," said Woody. "Not because you are a space ranger, because you're his toy!"

Maybe Woody was right. Maybe being a toy is important too.

The next day, with the help of Andy's toys, Woody and Buzz set out on a new escape mission.

One by one, each toy surrounded Sid and spoke to him. Sid was terrified! His days of torturing toys was over. The toys were free!

Buzz and Woody didn't have a second to celebrate. They could hear the rumble of removal vans outside Andy's house. It was moving day, and Andy's car was already disappearing down the road!

Buzz suddenly remembered Sid's rocket on his back. He might not be a real-life space hero, but toys can still be heroes!

With a whoosh, the friends fired the rocket straight towards Andy's car.

"Buzz, you're … flying!" gasped Woody.

"This isn't flying …. this is falling with style," grinned Buzz.

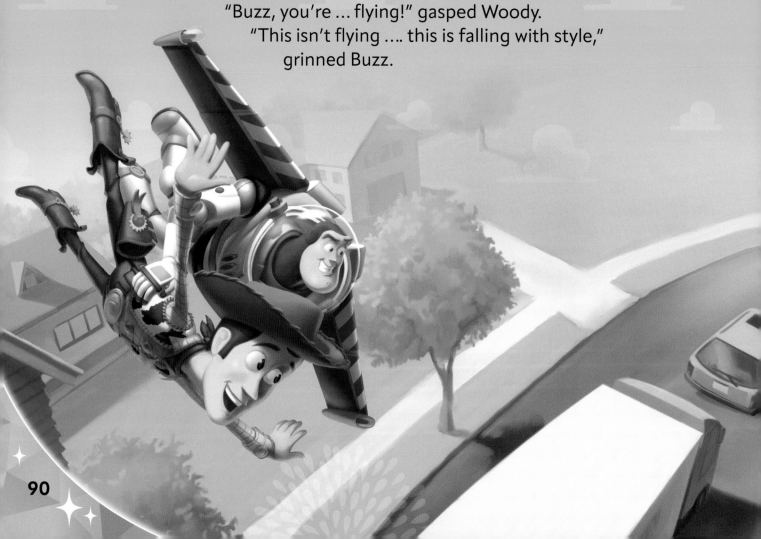

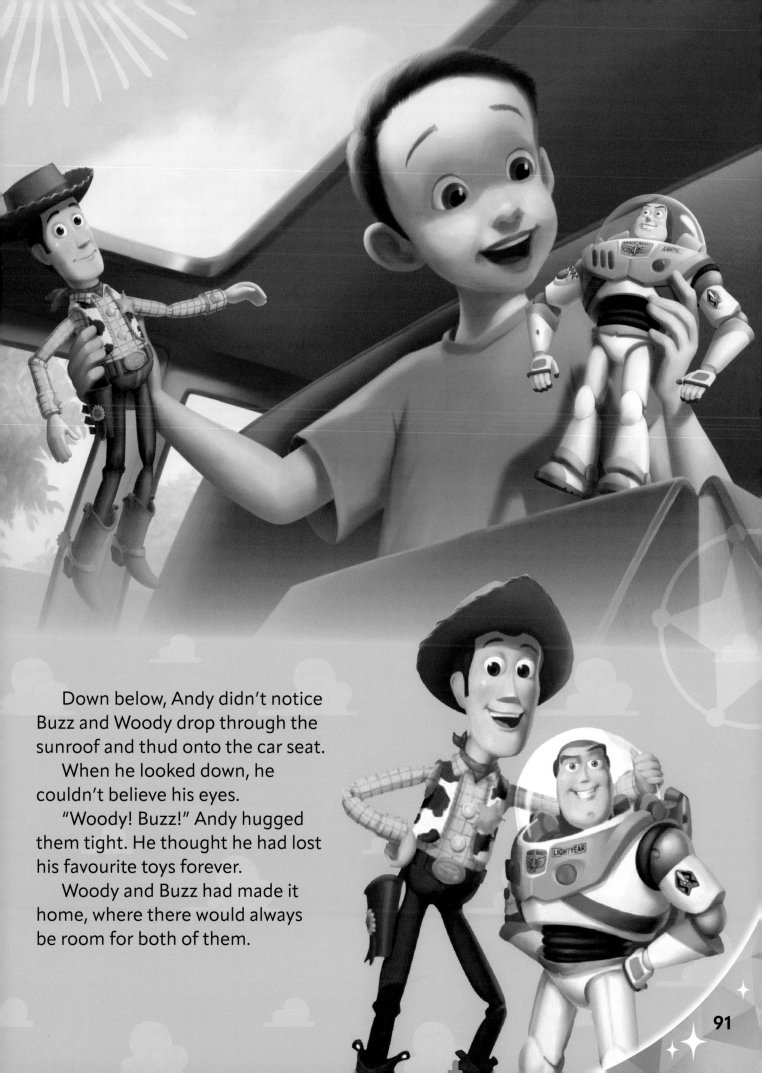

Down below, Andy didn't notice Buzz and Woody drop through the sunroof and thud onto the car seat.

When he looked down, he couldn't believe his eyes.

"Woody! Buzz!" Andy hugged them tight. He thought he had lost his favourite toys forever.

Woody and Buzz had made it home, where there would always be room for both of them.

Rescue Woody

Woody has been kidnapped by Al, and Buzz and the gang have set out to find him. Play the rescue game with a friend and see who is the first to save Woody.

Use a counter to move along the board. Take turns rolling a dice and move the counter as many spaces as the number you throw. If you land on a space with a picture on it, follow the instructions in the key.

Ready gang? Let's go!

How many soldiers are hiding in the grass? Colour them in.

START

1 2 3 4 5 6 7 8 9 10 11 12 13

14 15 16 17 18 19 20 21 22 23 24 25 26 27 28

FINISH

Howdy! Thanks for rescuing me.

AL's TOY BARN

KEY

You meet Bullseye and he gives you a ride. **Move forward 1 space!**

You stumble upon a ball, and have to stay and play. **Skip your turn!**

There are roadworks ahead, and you must find another route. **Move back 1 space!**

93

Meet the Crew

Are you ready to race around the track to meet the *Cars* crew? Let's go!

Lightning McQueen

Number 95 Lightning McQueen is a hotshot race car. His rookie days might be past him, but he can still rip up the racetrack!

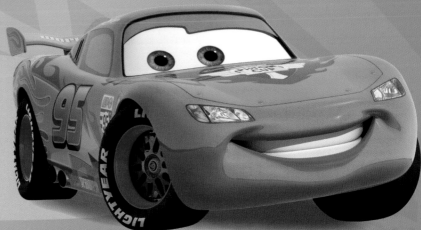

Mater

Dusty, rusty Mater is the heart and soul of Radiator Springs. He gets into a whole lot of scrapes, but this funny tow truck is Lightning McQueen's most loyal sidekick.

Sally Carrera

When Sally got tired of her busy life in California, she started a new life in Radiator Springs. Now she is happy to be cruising in the slow lane with Lightning and her new friends.

94

Fillmore

Easy-going and peace-loving Fillmore sells his own eco-friendly fuel and tie-dye mud flaps in his shop. He is proud to be part of Lightning McQueen's pit crew.

Finn McMissile

This master spy is an expert in daredevil escapes. Loaded with grappling hooks and a missile launcher, the bad guys are no match for Finn and his ultra-cool gadgets.

Francesco Bernoulli

Number 1 Bernoulli is Italy's top racer and Lightning McQueen's rival in the World Grand Prix. Everyone loves this stylish speeder, but Francesco's biggest fan is definitely himself!

Time Trials

The race is on! Speed down each twisty track to find out who wins the trophy.

96

Answers on page 117.

The Big Clean-up

Radiator Springs is in a big mess today. Can you help Mater clean up the town?

Circle these objects when you spot them in the big picture.

Answers on page 117.

Finding Nemo

Listen to the story about this little lost fish. When you see a picture join in and say the word!

 Nemo   Marlin   ocean

 Dory   sharks   sea turtle

When a little clownfish named 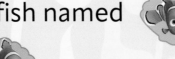 went missing

from his home, , his dad went on an epic

adventure to save him. was scared to swim

across the , but he met a funny fish named

 who helped him.

On their way, and met a group of

friendly . They promised not to eat them. "Fish

are friends, not food!" the chanted. They also

met a very cool , who guided them on their way.

"Now, turn your fishy tails 'round and swim straight on

through to Sydney!" shouted the .

Meanwhile, was stuck in a dentist's fish tank in Sydney Harbour, where he had made some new friends.

was scared, but he knew his dad was coming to rescue him. and the other tank fish hatched a plan to escape.

and had finally arrived in Sydney Harbour. With the help of a friendly pelican, they were able to fly up and see in the dentist's office, just in time to see him get flushed down a toilet!

Thankfully, all drains lead to the sea. escaped to the and was found by and his dad. told his son about all his adventures. couldn't believe his dad met and a !

Monster Mix

So many Mikes! Can you spot these three Mikes in the big monster mix?

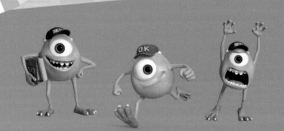

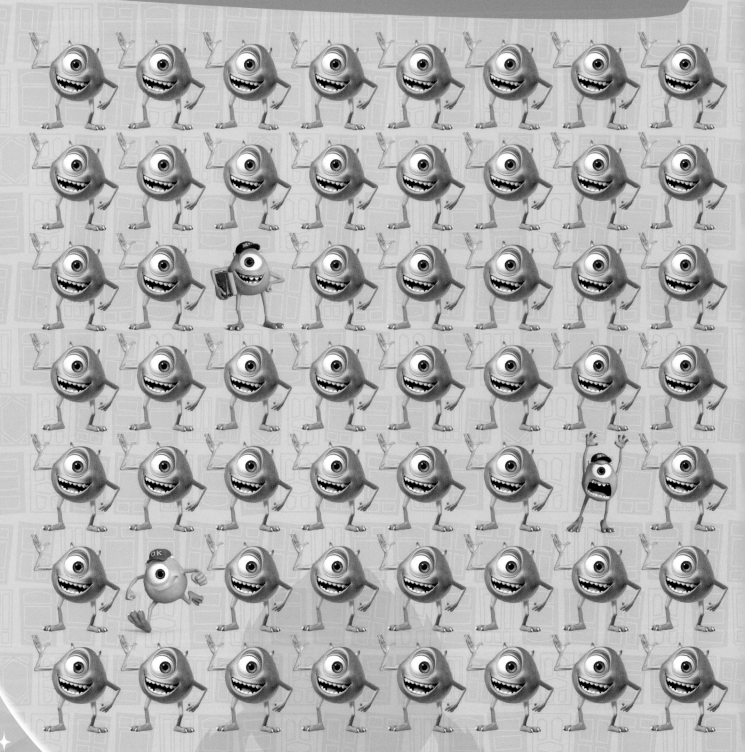

Answers on page 117.

My Monster

Imagine a fun, furry, friendly monster is behind your door. Draw it!

Super Mask

A Super's identity is their most secret weapon. Make your own Super mask to keep your identity a secret.

You will need:
- tracing paper
- pencil
- coloured card
- scissors
- hole punch
- glue
- string

Ask a grown-up for help when using scissors.

1   Trace the template from the next page onto paper and stick it onto coloured card.

2   Cut out your mask shape. Ask an adult to cut out the eye holes for you and use a hole punch to make holes for the string.

3   Using a different colour of card, draw and cut out shapes to stick to your mask. Add glitter, sequins and buttons – anything you can find at home to make your mask special.

4   Thread string through the holes and tie in a knot at the front to keep them secure. Ask an adult to fix the mask on for you and tie it up at the back.

Now, you're ready to save the day!

103

Power Up

The Incredibles have made a super game, just for you. Can you power up, throw the dice and take the challenge? Keep rolling until you have done them all!

1 Run on the spot for 20 seconds.

2 Give somebody a hug or a high-five.

3 Help to tidy up.

4 Dance for 20 seconds.

5 Make a picture.

6 Dress up as a superhero.

Made to Play!

Need for Speed!

Fun Facts

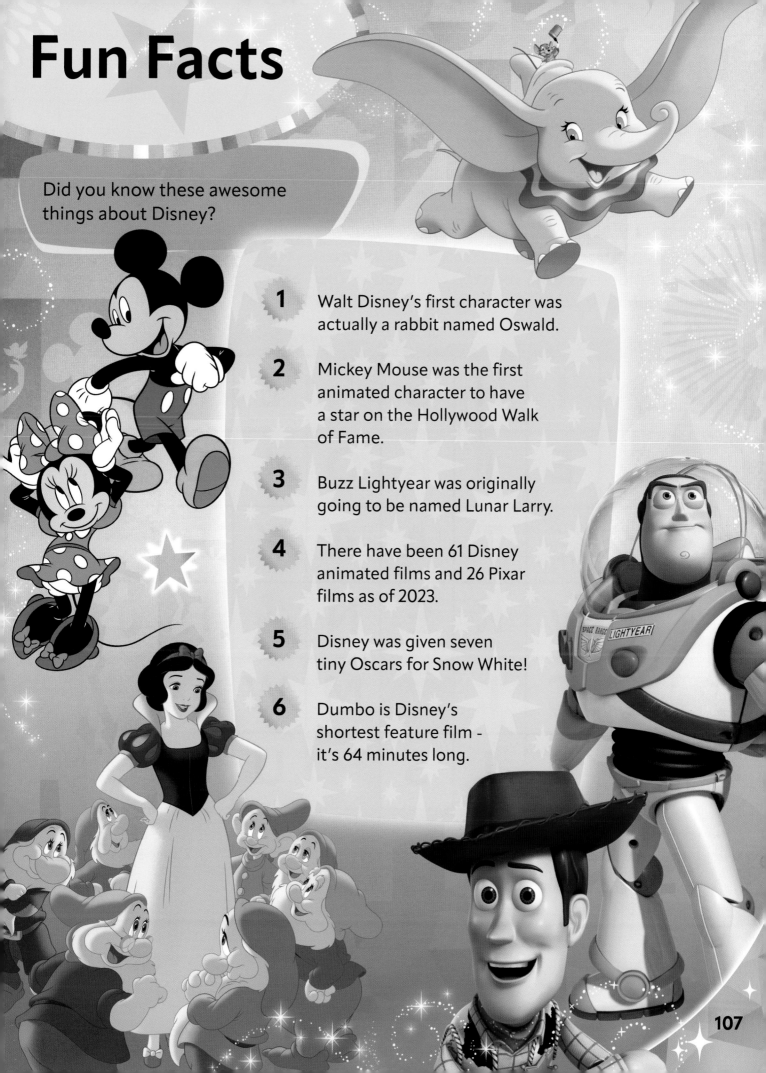

Did you know these awesome things about Disney?

1 Walt Disney's first character was actually a rabbit named Oswald.

2 Mickey Mouse was the first animated character to have a star on the Hollywood Walk of Fame.

3 Buzz Lightyear was originally going to be named Lunar Larry.

4 There have been 61 Disney animated films and 26 Pixar films as of 2023.

5 Disney was given seven tiny Oscars for Snow White!

6 Dumbo is Disney's shortest feature film - it's 64 minutes long.

Home, Sweet Home

Where does WALL•E live?
Travel around the grid using the directions below.
Pick up a letter each time you stop. Write down the
letters to discover WALL•E's home.

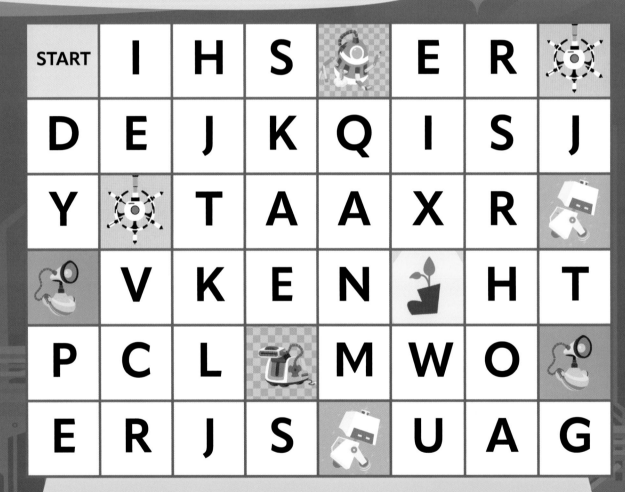

START | I | H | S | | E | R |
D | E | J | K | Q | I | S | J
Y | | T | A | A | X | R |
| V | K | E | N | | H | T
P | C | L | | M | W | O |
E | R | J | S | | U | A | G

1. Go down
5 spaces.

2. Go right
6 spaces.

3. Go up
3 spaces.

4. Go left
4 spaces.

5. Go up
2 spaces.

WALL•E lives on ....

Answers on page 117.

108

Invent-a-bot

WALL•E is built for picking up rubbish and keeping things tidy. Can you invent a cool robot to help you? Design it here!

Robot name:

....

Robot helps me with:

....

Odd Olaf Out

If only there was more Olaf to go around, but there can only be one! Which picture below is the odd one out and the real beloved snowman?

1

2

3

4

5

6

110

Answers on page 117.

A Snowy Spot

Anna loves ice skating!
Can you find five differences
in picture 2 below?

Snowballs and Snowslides

There's a winter party in the Enchanted Forest, but Anna and Elsa are running late. Challenge a friend to see who can reach the party first.

You will need:

- 2 players
- A dice
- Counters (you could use coins, paper or little toys)

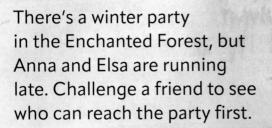

Elsa

Anna

33

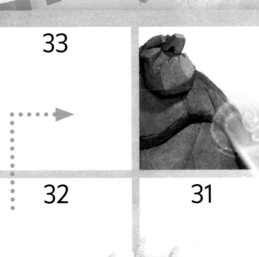

35

32

31

18

19

15

1

3

START

How to play:

- Decide who will be Elsa and who will be Anna.
- Take turns to roll the dice and move forward the number rolled.
- If you land on Olaf's snowballs, climb up the board.
- If you land on Earth Giant's snowslides, whizz back down the board.
- The first one to the party is the winner!

FINISH

36	37	38		40
29			26	25
20	21	22	23	
13	12	11		9
4	5		7	8

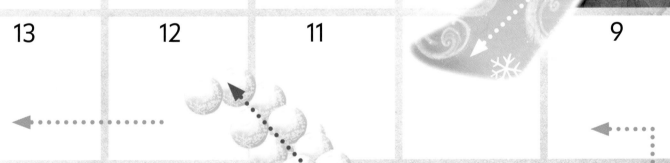

A Party Wish

Imagine your dream party. Who would you invite? Where would it be? What would you eat? Let's get planning and make your party wish list.

Guest List

Eve

Eilidh

Seurrah

Katie   amygrace

kealie   wykb

donna   cull

mark   skye

Where? (the place)

....

....

When?

day time ☐

night time ☐

Theme

panda

football culy thistle

Decorations

Design more party bunting.

Party bag

Draw two things to go inside your dream party bag.

phone   teddySalat as

Cake

Design your dream cake!

panda

panda

panda

Surprise!

Ssh … write down one big surprise to wow your guests.

....

....

Answers

Page 12
Party Problem

Page 13
Mickey's Wordsearch

X	P	A	E	L	D	R	Z	E	Q
M	E	W	X	W	O	T	T	R	U
I	Y	L	M	I	N	N	I	E	F
C	K	S	O	G	A	X	C	I	J
K	U	P	Z	R	L	W	T	U	H
E	M	L	N	U	D	A	I	S	Y
Y	E	U	B	H	S	S	Q	Y	E
T	O	T	U	M	G	A	W	D	I
Y	F	O	O	G	Z	T	L	E	A
E	W	H	Q	Z	X	A	Y	J	E

Page 14
Super Sizes
1. b
2. a

3. | 1 | 3 | 2 |

4. | 3 | 1 | 2 |

Page 15
Animal Alphabet
snake   monkey   panther
bear   elephant

Page 16
Follow Your Heart
Path 3 leads to Jasmine.

Page 17
Magic Count

I count 10 lamps.

Page 18
Down the Rabbit Hole

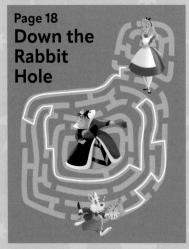

Pages 20-21
Puppy Pairs
1 - b, 2 - a, 3 - f, 4 - d, 5 - h,
6 - c, 7 - g, 8 - i, 9 - e.

Page 24
Starry Shadows
1 - c, 2 - d, 3 - b, 4 - a.

Page 26
Pinocchio Patterns

Page 27
Puzzle Pals

Page 29
The Way Back Home

Page 38
Story Quiz
1. c, 2. a, 3. b, 4. a, 5. a.

Page 39
Count Along

| 3 | 5 | 2 | 7 | 4 | 9 | 6 |

Page 40
Jigsaw Jumble

Page 43
Pet Puzzle

116

Page 50
Stronger Together

Page 51
Magical Madrigal Memory
1. True, 2. False, 3. True, 4. False, 5. False.

Page 54
Tell the Time

6 o'clock   7 o'clock   8 o'clock

Page 56
A Christmas Wish

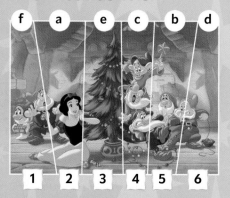

f a e c b d

1 2 3 4 5 6

Page 57
Who's Who?
Doc - 3, Grumpy - 5, Happy - 2, Sneezy - 6, Dopey - 4, Bashful - 1, Sleepy - 7.

Page 66
Helpful Friends

Page 70
Belle's Rose
1. a $6 + 3 = 9$
   b $2 + 3 = 5$
   c $5 + 3 = 8$
2.

Page 71
A Snowy Mission
Path 3 leads to the Beast.

Page 72
Odd One Out
1. c, 2. b, 3. d.

Page 76
Finding Friends
Path c

Page 77
Count with Ariel
Box b has the most things.

Page 78
Rapunzel's Round-up

appears the most.

Page 79
Chameleon Colours
1. b, 2. c,
3.

Page 80
Fairy Fun
1.

2. c, 3. c.

Page 92
Rescue Woody
4 soldiers.

Page 96
Time Trials
Lightning McQueen wins the trophy on path 2.

Page 97
The Big Clean-up

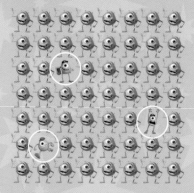

Page 100
Monster Mix

Page 108
Home, Sweet Home

I	H	S		E	R	
D	E	J	K	Q	I	S	J
Y		T	A	A	X	R	
	V	K	E	N		H	T
P	C	L		M	W	O	
	E	R	J	S		U	A	G

WALL•E lives on EARTH.

Page 110
Odd Olaf Out
Picture 5 is the odd one out.

Page 111
A Snowy Spot

117